Books by Marie Stopes, D.Sc., Ph. D.

SEXOLOGY

MARRIED LOVE. 18th edition. Published by Putnam. 6s. net.

RADIANT MOTHERHOOD. 4th edition. Published by Putnam. 6s. net.

TRUTH ABOUT VENEREAL DISEASE. 5th Imp. Published by Putnam. Cloth, 3s. 6d. net.

A LETTER TO WORKING MOTHERS. Published by the Author. 3rd edition. 3d. net.

EARLY DAYS OF BIRTH CONTROL. Published by Putnam. 9d. net.

MOTHER, HOW WAS I BORN? Published by Putnam. 6d. net.

CONTRACEPTION: ITS THEORY, HISTORY, AND PRACTICE. Illustrated. Published by John Bale, Sons, and Danielsson. 2nd edition. 15s. net.

SEX AND THE YOUNG. Gill, 6s. 6d.

THE HUMAN BODY. Illustrated. Gill, 6s. 6d.

BIOLOGICAL

THE CRETACEOUS FLORA, Part I. Illustrated. Published by the Trustees of the British Museum. 12s. net.

THE CRETACEOUS FLORA, Part II. Illustrated. Published by the Trustees of the British Museum. £1 1s. net.

ANCIENT PLANTS. Illustrated. Published by Blackie. 7s. 6d. net.

THE STUDY OF PLANT LIFE. 2nd edition. Illustrated. Published by Blackie. 3s. 6d. net.

TRAVEL

A JOURNAL FROM JAPAN. Published by Blackie. 7s. 6d. net.

LITERARY

MAN, OTHER POEMS, AND A PREFACE. Published by Heinemann. 3s. 6d. net.

CONQUEST, a Three-Act Play. Published by French. 1s. net.

GOLD IN THE WOOD and THE RACE. Two Plays. Published by Fifield. 2s. net.

PLAYS OF OLD JAPAN, THE NŌ, with Prof. J. Sakurai. Published by Heinemann. 5s. net.

OUR OSTRICHES, a Play. Published by Putnam. 2s. net.

The author's vivid and imaginative sympathy has really enabled her in some degree to communicate the incommunicable.

ATHENÆUM.

WISE PARENTHOOD

A PRACTICAL SEQUEL TO

MARRIED LOVE

WISE PARENTHOOD

THE TREATISE ON BIRTH CONTROL FOR MARRIED PEOPLE. A PRACTICAL SEQUEL TO "MARRIED LOVE"

BY

MARIE CARMICHAEL STOPES

Doctor of Science, London; Doctor of Philosophy, Munich; Fellow of University College, London; Fellow of the Royal Society of Literature, and of the Linnean and Geological Societies, London

With an Introduction by
ARNOLD BENNETT

FIFTEENTH EDITION
Revised and Enlarged
496th Thousand

LONDON: G. P. PUTNAM'S SONS
24 BEDFORD STREET, STRAND, W.C.2

EDITIONS

First published	*November* 18, 1918
Second Edition	*January*, 1919
Third Edition	*March*, 1919
Fourth Edition	*April*, 1919
Fifth Edition	*August*, 1919
Reprinted once	
Sixth Edition	*July*, 1920
Reprinted twice	
Seventh Edition . . .	*June*, 1921
Reprinted once	
Eighth Edition . . .	*May*, 1922
Ninth Edition	*September*, 1922
Tenth Edition	*December*, 1922
Reprinted three times	
Eleventh Edition . . .	*March*, 1923
Reprinted eight times	
Twelfth Edition . . .	*October*, 1923
Reprinted sixteen times	
Thirteenth Edition . . .	*March*, 1927
Fourteenth Edition . . .	*August*, 1927
Fifteenth Edition . . .	*February*, 1928
Reprinted . . .	*May*, 1928

Completing 496 *Thousand*

TRANSLATIONS

Danish
Swedish
German
Dutch
Czech
Spanish
Hungarian

MADE IN GREAT BRITAIN

Dedicated to all who wish to see our race grow in strength and beauty

Introductory Note

THE rapid progress of the idea of birth regulation is one of the outstanding social phenomena of the time. But it cannot astonish the thoughtful, for the idea appeals almost irresistibly to the common sense and the conscience of civilised beings, and nothing save superstition and ignorance can impair or impede its triumph. Further, everybody knows that the vast majority of its instructed opponents practise in their private lives what they condemn for others. That birth regulation has disadvantages is arguable. Its disadvantages, however, are not those usually emphasised by its opponents. For example, no unprejudiced brain will contend that that which is so manifestly beneficent to the individual can be bad for the race. Nor have children hitherto been such a source of sorrow and disappointment to parents that the parental instinct is likely to be destroyed through the temptations of any device whatever. No! The disadvantages of birth regulation are mainly transient; they spring from an imperfect acquaintance with the methods of it; and they will pass. Millions and tens of millions of potential parents need advice about birth regulation. They cry out for sound advice, and they do not get it. They suffer, sometimes horribly, for want of sound advice. This book is a practical manual of birth regulation written by an unchallenged authority for the intimate use of potential parents.

ARNOLD BENNETT.

Author's Preface

THE origin of this book was an attempt to answer innumerable inquirers who, having read "Married Love" (first published in 1918), approached me desiring wholesome information on a subject of vital importance to themselves and to the race. Not only these individual inquirers, but the world at large, and even the medical profession, lacked a rational, scientific and critical consideration of the details concerning the methods for the control of conception, some of which are now so widely used. My book seemed urgently needed, because owing to this very lack of serious and scientific presentation, ill-informed and often debased instruction had been circulating freely.

And even the one British society then (1918) advocating control of conception, namely, the Malthusian League, distributed to inquirers an all too brief leaflet giving indiscriminate instructions, including, without sufficient critical examination or physiological caution, such methods as *coitus interruptus*, and advising douching (see p. 68). Some users observed for themselves that these methods are harmful; and the mistaken idea gained currency that these were representative methods, hence that "methods are harmful," and hence that the advocacy of birth control implies the advocacy of harmful methods. I am convinced by experience that much of the opposition to "methods" is due to the confusion thus created in prudish minds incapable of distinguishing between harmful methods and wholesome ones, yet vaguely aware that some methods *are* harmful.

In July, 1922, the above-named Society issued a revised leaflet (now a small pamphlet), re-written by Norman Haire, Esq., M.B., who follows the main thesis of my book, viz., that an internal rubber cap worn by the woman is the best contraceptive for general use. That he favours a different form of cap (the Dutch hemispherical type) is a minor, though not unimportant, point which will be dealt with in the following pages (see p. 49).

Owing to a variety of circumstances which have fostered ignorance and strengthened prejudice, the subject of the control of conception has not hitherto received that learned attention which its importance deserves; but for long there have been scattered in the medical and scientific journals and treatises, and in other and more intimately human records, facts based on more or less isolated experience which, once correlated, are sufficient at any rate to form a basis for the kind of critical consideration which is wanted. The ethical, the romantic, the physiological, the frankly practical and economic aspects, and the distantly ramifying results of the various methods, are all of vital importance and are essentially interwoven. Though one or the other may have received some attention, those who have pronounced their opinions for or against the control of conception have hitherto generally done so without specifying to which means they refer, and often without taking into consideration the conflicting needs of different aspects of the life of even one individual. Without making an elaborate treatise of this book, all these points have been borne in mind while writing it.

As is indicated in the title-page, the Fourteenth Edition has been revised, and certain changes which will I hope add to its usefulness, and a certain number of new passages, have been added. Since it was first written in 1918 it has had an enormous number of readers, many of whom have written to me confirming, and often illustrating from their own lives, the generalisations presented in its pages. Moreover, many of the readers have been medical men who have cordially endorsed its teaching.

Further practical knowledge has accrued concerning the subject of Contraception as a result of the founding of the pioneer Birth Control Clinic. To the Clinic have come many thousands of cases whose requirements have been investigated. In connection with public meetings and various private conferences, I have also had the advantage of discussions on the subject with numerous medical practitioners of different nationalities. Yet the main teachings of this book, as published in 1918, remain not only unshaken, but strengthened.

Inquiry and investigation have not resulted in the discovery of any method better for normal women than the use of the simple all-rubber cap described in the following pages. An improved form of greasy suppository to combine with it is now the reward of our work at the Clinic, and the fourteenth edition was the first to hand on to the public information about it (see p. 42). Research should be pursued, but it seems clear that no very revolutionary result in the field of simple contraceptive measures is imminent. Injections to produce temporary sterility, the use of X-rays, and other methods, suitable only for use by medical specialists, are those attracting attention in advanced circles, but they are not at present of any widespread practical use.

At the request of several distinguished medical men, some years ago I began to write a comprehensive manual on the subject, because none such exists in any language.

This has now been completed, and is published by Messrs. Bale and Danielsson under the title "Contraception (Birth Control), Its Theory, History and Practice: A Manual for the Medical and Legal Professions." Educated readers who require more detailed information than the present small volume contains will find it useful and written in sufficiently non-technical language. Its perusal should answer many questions frequently asked.

In the preparation of the present small book I have been indebted to very many men and women who have voluntarily confided to me their personal experiences and needs, thus supplying me with invaluable facts. My thanks are due to the late Professor E. H. Starling, C.M.G., F.R.S., who, in 1919, while disclaiming any responsibility for this book, and even in various details definitely dissenting from my conclusions, read the early proof and gave me the benefit of his valuable opinions. The Rev. Sir James Marchant, K.B.E., F.R.S.Edin., and Dr. Mary Scharlieb, C.B.E., M.S., also very kindly read the proofs of an early edition, and I have benefited by their suggestions, although we disagree on fundamental principles.

Personal instruction about individual procedure will still be wanted by many, particularly where slightly abnormal formations or induced malformations render prevention difficult; and I ardently believe that Clinics should be within reach of all, so that rightly trained midwives, nurses and doctors, of suitably sympathetic temperament, can be applied to personally for help.

Realising that this, like most books, will only be of use to the educated and more thoughtful people, and that it is of great racial urgency to bring this knowledge to the poorest and least literate section of the community, my husband Mr. H. V. Roe and I opened the first Birth Control Clinic in the British Empire in March, 1921, in a poor district in Holloway, London, N. For the convenience of its many visitors, in 1925 it was removed to more central quarters at 108, Whitfield Street, Tottenham Court Road, W.1. This Clinic is open daily without charge to all married persons, and has been used by great numbers of poor mothers as well as by members of the medical and nursing professions who desire the information and help I am always glad to give.

At the present date nearly ten thousand cases have come personally to the Clinic, and hundreds of thousands of applications by post from all parts of the world have been dealt with by sending practical advice, doctors' addresses, pamphlets and literature. Of those who have come for personal examination, and who have been helped, the first five thousand case sheets have been analysed and published in a little book at 2s. 6d. under the title of "The First Five Thousand," which those who are interested in the details of the Clinic work should find valuable reading.

On the day the Clinic was opened we framed and placed upon the wall the following:—

> "THIS CLINIC IS FREE TO ALL, and is supported entirely by the two founders. Those who have benefited by its help are asked to hand on knowledge of its existence to others and help to create a public opinion which will force the Ministry of Health to include a similar service in Ante-Natal and Welfare Centres already supported by the Government in every district."

And it is gratifying indeed to feel that official representatives of all political parties, a great many independent Societies, and even the House of Lords itself by passing Lord Buckmaster's motion in 1926, show that they have rapidly come round to our way of thinking.

The new era which is now dawning should —must—be one in which the people are supplied with sound knowledge to meet their needs. Knowledge on many subjects which has been kept obscure to the past generation is reaching the public in garbled form. Only if those of scientific spirit who possess the nearest approach to truth which is at the time available will assist each other in spreading the truth, can the public be really helped and enlightened. For this reason, in 1921, I felt that it would be wise to knit together in a definite organisation some of the more public spirited of the many people who showed themselves alive to the significance of true and scientific sex-knowledge. The Society for Constructive Birth Control and Racial Progress was organised, and held its first general meeting in October, 1921. A list of its officers and some other particulars about it will be found in the flyleaf of this book. A sister Society in America, the Voluntary Parenthood League,[1] has a heavier task than ours, as it has not merely to educate public opinion, but to effect a change of Federal Law before real practical work can be done in the States. All who care for true human progress should join one, or preferably both, of these Societies, for the English-speaking nations are so closely linked that in this matter they should co-operate.

I have daily evidence that already this little book is of use all the world over, and I hope it may help to improve our race, and to check the spread of nervous and other injuries sadly prevalent as a result of ignorant attempts to obtain that wise and health-giving control of parenthood which all who think must crave.

While it is far from being an *exhaustive* treatise, and while it is deliberately written in

[1] V.P.L. Director, Mrs. Mary Ware Dennett. Address: St. Denis Building, Broadway, New York City.

non-technical and clear English, it was the first scientific and critical consideration of the practical aspects of the subject which, as Lord Dawson said at the Church Congress, in October, 1921, "has come to stay."

I should like to take this opportunity of urging young couples who truly love, to have all the children to whom they can give health and beauty, even if by doing so they sacrifice their personal luxuries.

M. C. S.

1927.

WISE PARENTHOOD

Chapter I

"I think, dearest Uncle, you cannot *really* wish me to be the '*Mamma d'une nombreuse famille*,' for I think you will see the great inconvenience a *large* family would be to us all, and particularly to the country, independent of the hardship and inconvenience to myself. Men never think, at least seldom think, what a hard task it is for us women to go through this *very often*."—QUEEN VICTORIA in a letter to the King of the Belgians, January 15, 1841.

A FAMILY of healthy happy children should be the joy of every pair of married lovers. To-day more than ever the course of duty and delight coincide for those who have health and love in their homes. For to-day as never before the world needs the products of sound and beautiful love, and though these range from the intangible aroma of peace and happiness which a rightly wedded pair radiate, through an infinite variety of spiritual and physical results, the most vital and the most potentially valuable to the community are the children.

Whatever theory of the transmission of characteristics scientists may ultimately adopt, there can be little doubt in the minds of rational people that heredity *does* tell, and that children who descend from a double line of healthy and intelligent parents are better equipped to face whatever difficulties in their environment may later arise than are children from unsound stock. As Sir James Barr said in the *British Medical Journal*, 1918: "There is no equality in nature among children nor among adults, and if there is to be a much-needed improvement in the race, we must breed from the physically, morally and intellectually fit."

Nevertheless, the happiness which children should be in a home depends less on a conscious sense of civic virtue (though that may be a factor), than on an acute and warm personal feeling of the parents towards each other. Every man who finds beauty and goodness in his wife must feel a keen desire to repeat that beauty and goodness throughout all time, and every woman who has picked her mate freely, and because she thought him a knight among men, must long to see his characteristics reproduced, so that the world should not lose the imprint of his splendour when the inevitable happens and he has to pass. Indeed, one may almost take it as an axiom when dealing with true love that the pair do feel thus towards each other, and consequently desire children, unless they are aware that either is stricken by some inherent weakness or disease which might reappear in the child. Then they must refrain from parenthood out of a sense of duty and pity towards the unborn.

Nature herself provided that men and women should delight in meeting. Given a loving married pair in normal health, and unsophisticated in any way, there is seldom any lack of children around them after they have been wedded for some years. This is what is still described as the "natural" condition of affairs, and in these days of sophistication in so-called "civilisation," some reformers urge a return to Nature and an unregulated birth-rate.

If, however, the course of "nature" is allowed to run unguided, babies come in general too quickly for the resources of most, and particularly of city-dwelling, families, and the parents as well as the children consequently suffer. Wise parents therefore guide nature, and control the conception of the desired children so as to space them in the way best adjusted to what health, wealth, and happiness they have to give. The object of this book is to tell prospective parents how best to do this, and to hand on to them in a concise form what help science can give on this vital subject.

This is not an attempt to present complete arguments to show the racial and national necessity for the Control of Conception: various aspects of this theme have been presented by others.

Recently valuable expositions of the supreme importance to humanity of a wise use of the control of conception have been made from many different points of view and by various distinguished people. Doubtless much more remains to be said, for there are many who are still ignorant, and consequently prejudiced against the greatest of the steps humanity can take next in its evolution; but this is not the place to deal with the wider aspects of the subject.

That a large proportion of intelligent and thoughtful married couples are practising at the present moment some method or other of the control of conception is beyond dispute. In Lord Dawson of Penn's speech before the Church Congress at Birmingham in 1921 he said: "I will put forward with confidence the view that birth control is here to stay. It is an established fact, and for good or evil has to be accepted. Although the extent of its application can be and is being modified, no denunciations will abolish it." The question before us, therefore, is not whether or no some knowledge of contraceptives should be allowed; it is already established. General dissatisfaction with most of the methods used is however prevalent; and this dissatisfaction is not being alleviated, because there is also a widespread ignorance of satisfactory methods, even on the part of medical practitioners. Numbers of people who are practising and have been practising the control of conception by various means for years, are in urgent need of a better method than any known to them. The following pages are written for them.

. . . . .

If this book gets into the hands of some who have not given the subject of the control of conception adequate thought they should read the books mentioned on pp. 83–84. This short list is only representative of a few of the more important aspects of the subject; but if a serious student is not yet convinced by them and will follow up and read all the other works referred to in them, he will then at any rate have a fair idea of the essentials of the subject and can form his own opinions.

What we are here concerned with is the fact that contraceptive methods of all sorts are now so widely used that it is high time serious attention should be devoted to the subject. People should not be employing anything less satisfactory than the best now obtainable; but, unless they are given the best, they will assuredly use some less desirable means.

I will give a quotation from one of our most

ardent social reformers. The Rev. Sir J. Marchant, Secretary of the Birth Rate Commission and Director of the National Council of Public Morals, in his book, "Birth Rate and Empire," says as follows (pp. 144–146):

> If, then, the volitional control of births within the married state has become a normal proceeding, if it is fast losing its apparent indelicacy, if it is spoken about without raising vicious passions, if it is becoming the "correct thing" to do . . . we must give up the futile attempt to keep young people in the dark and the assumption that they are ignorant of notorious facts. We cannot, if we would, stop the spread of sexual knowledge; and, if we could do so, we should only make matters infinitely worse. This is the second decade of the twentieth century, not the early Victorian period. . . . It is, then, no longer a question of knowing or not knowing. We have to disabuse our middle-aged minds of that fond delusion. Our young people know more than we did when we began our married lives, and sometimes as much as we know ourselves, even now. So that we need not continue to shake our few remaining hairs in simulating feelings of surprise and horror. It might have been better for us if we had been more enlightened. And if our discussion of this problem is to be of any real use, we must at the outset reconcile ourselves to the facts that the birth-rate is voluntarily controlled, that brides and bridegrooms know how it is done, and many will certainly do it. Certain persons who instruct us in these matters may hold up their pious hands and whiten their frightened faces as they cry out in the public squares against "this vice," but they only make themselves ridiculous. Their influence in stemming the tide is nearly *nil*.

The Rev. Sir J. Marchant says, "Brides and bridegrooms know how it is done." That is true. They know some, perhaps several, ways of securing voluntary instead of involuntary parenthood, but very few have precise and satisfactory knowledge of, or understand the reasons against, many of the methods which are recommended to them either by medical men or by friends who, as ignorant as they themselves, have been in the habit of using methods described as "harmless," simply because they do no gross and obvious injury.

Many things are reckoned "harmless" which are nevertheless far from satisfactory. Let me take an illustration from another aspect of our lives. Every medical man would consider doses of a half-teaspoonful of ammoniated quinine as not only harmless but beneficial to a patient suffering from influenza. Nevertheless, some even in normal health find that a few such doses upset the digestion for several weeks. It is true that in an influenza epidemic it may be more important to order quinine than to think about people's digestions, and in this sense quinine is not only "harmless" but beneficial. There are many parallels to this in the use of various kinds of preventives which are described as "harmless."

It is amazing that medical and physiological science should have so neglected research on this most vital subject, and that a more perfect procedure should not yet have been devised: it is perhaps more amazing that the reactions and results of the methods now widely used should not have been thoroughly studied and understood. The methods which I have to suggest are not yet the ideal, but they are much simpler, more healthful and less disillusioning than those most in vogue before this book was written. I am glad to think it has materially changed current practice.

After giving the details necessary for the comprehension and employment of the best methods which I can recommend, I shall mention one or two others of those in general use, with reasons why I think them inadvisable save in very special circumstances. The large number of other and still less satisfactory means employed will not be touched upon at all, as this is not a monographic dissertation, but an attempt to be helpful by presenting, if not the ideal, at any rate the good in place of the less good or actually bad.

A few fortunate people who really understand their own physiology, or by happy instinct have chanced upon the right use of their bodies and have been in the habit of practising satisfactory methods, may say or think that such simple and direct instruction as follows is not needed. I have, however, overwhelming evidence and experience that ignorance is rife even in the very places where knowledge might be expected to hold sway. For some time past, scarcely a day has gone by without my receiving letter after letter from people who have long been married, from people who have consulted physicians, from people who have tried many experiments, and who are yet ignorant of any really *satisfactory* means of achieving what they have been perforce achieving in unsatisfactory ways. I once asked a medical woman who had had a practice for fifteen years what method she would advise: she knew of no method whatever. A well-known doctor in London, who for twenty years had had a general and important family practice, asked me if I could tell him of any method other than the sheath, which was the only one he knew, as his patients were inquiring and he did not know what to tell them. Many married couples, who are even told by the doctor that for the wife to have another child would be fatal, are at the same time not told any rational method of prevention. With variations depending on the temperament of the writer, I get appeals one after the other saying: "We have asked our doctor, but he tells us nothing which is of any use. We have therefore to go on using this, that, or the other method, which we feel to be unsatisfactory, because we do not know what else to do." In the pages which follow they will find an account of the physiological reactions of various methods and will thus be able to use the means best suited to their own circumstances.

Some churchmen recommend and some demand "absolute continence," save when a child is desired as a result of union. Where the mated pair are young, normal, and in love, such advice is not only impracticable, it is detrimental. Under such conditions a rigid and enforced abstinence, even where it is not directly injurious to health, may yet have as harmful effects as incontinence. The capacities and requirements of people vary greatly, and no universal rule can apply to all. Other clerics and ascetic-minded laymen sometimes disguise (perhaps even deceiving themselves) "absolute continence" under the more popular term of "self-control," which has a noble sound, and is liable, by credulous audiences, to be applauded. But "self-control" will not limit the numbers of the family unless it is so extensive that its correct description is "total abstinence extended over years," and this, as most medical men now agree, is not conducive to the physical well-being, or the mental harmony of a home composed of normal, strong and healthy young people, however suitable it may be for those ageing or of weak vitality. On the one side "absolute continence," and on the other an easy self-indulgence, are in married life equally to be condemned. In either of these two quagmires disasters lie in great variety. The narrow and safe path between them is a wise, reasoned and controlled use of the most intimate and sacred functions of the body.

Though for general guidance the suggestion which I have made, particularly in Chapter V of "Married Love," may be of service, yet each pair must find out for themselves the point where self-control becomes an object in itself and detrimental to health and vitality, and where on the other hand the expression of love begins to slide into a too facile indulgence.

My object is not to make sex-experience a danger-free indulgence, but to raise the sense of responsibility, the standard of self-control and knowledge which goes with maturity, and consequently the ultimate health and happiness of those who mate. It should be understood by the man, who is in general the more active partner, that he has to consider not only himself but his mate, and that *the only right rule in marriage is that which gives the greatest sum total of health and happiness to the two concerned, for the benefit of the nation and the race. To achieve this, most men will have to exercise a fine self-control, truly ennobling and strengthening both to mind and body.*

A knowledge of the means of prevention of conception may co-exist with low standards of living and personal hygiene, but even then such knowledge may save the next generation the misery of being hurled into wretched conditions, and may save the community the cost of maintaining anti-social lives.

Some, who would otherwise welcome the spread of knowledge on this important subject, fear an increase of promiscuous relations as a result. It appears, however, that the type of person who desires to lead an irregular life has long had access to sufficient information to satisfy such requirements, while the virtuous mother has been helpless in her ignorance of how to control her motherhood in the interests of her children. Daily experience at the Birth Control Clinic bears this out in a convincing manner. Hundreds of worn and wretchedly over-burdened mothers have applied for the help given by knowledge, but not a couple of flighty young people. The latter can get crude information from their companions.

Those who would debar the personally selfish from the knowledge of such methods of control, forget that it is just by those who do not trouble to *prevent* evils that the worst and most disastrous attempts are made to overtake the evils they themselves originated. I do not wish in this book to speak of the prevalence and horror of the poor and ignorant woman's attempts at early abortions: the story would be too heartrending, and is out of place in this little book, which is one of help and guidance.

Destructive of the health of both mother and

child are the frantic efforts of women "caught," prematurely after a birth, or too frequently in their lives, by undesired motherhood. The desolating effects of abortion and attempted abortion can only be exterminated by a sound knowledge of the control of conception. In this my message coincides with that of all the Churches in condemning utterly the taking of even an embryonic life.

Alas that so many ignorant women do not realise the difference between the control of conception and abortion, and for want of knowledge of the former are ruining their health and pouring money into the pockets of unscrupulous firms which sell "pills."

Chapter II

"All turns on what we say is included under divine law. If it is *de jure divino,* then there is no power to modify it; but if any portion is not, then there is power."

DOES divine law condemn scientific methods of controlling conception?

It does not.

And Christ never condemned parental control and voluntary parenthood.

The Churches, long after His words were spoken, concocted various views of the matter by combining the Pauline attitude toward sex with various Old Testament verses. But no Church, not even the Roman Catholic, has ever yet had a permanent, a logical, or a racially ennobling code of teaching on the subject. The pressure of public opinion is continually forcing the Churches in this, as in other matters, to shift their ground. Alas! While they endeavour to instruct and legislate, they do not lead.

The Memorandum of the Bishops of the

Anglican Catholic Church, the doctrine of the Roman Catholic Church, the pronouncement in congress of the main body of Christian Nonconformists, and the Jewish Church, have all very similarly condemned what they call "artificial" methods. The Roman Catholic Church in particular is the most unyielding in its total condemnation of the use of scientific aid in controlling the production of children, although it—like the other Churches—concedes the *principle* of the justifiability of control in some circumstances. To concede the principle, even while condemning the best methods of effecting such control, is to deny the uses of intellectual progress. The stricter members of the Churches obey their edicts; or, with uneasy or unhappy consciences, disobey because they must, or because their training and intelligence teach them that they should make use of what scientific knowledge is available for their help. Hence numbers of Roman Catholics defy the priests or conceal from them the fact that they use methods of control. An interesting example of a particularly self-reliant and brave Roman Catholic who not only privately but openly defied his priest and publicly advocated birth control is reported in his own words in the *Birth Control News* for April, 1927, vol. v, No. 12. Some priests permit methods and themselves deny the authority of the Church, all of which indicates the nation's hunger for intelligent help on lines suited to modern conditions.

The wisdom of the Churches is ancient and pre-scientific: humanity to-day is modern and lives under increasingly "artificial" conditions: only the divinely-given everlasting truths are eternal, and on these the Churches must base their authority. Are any such divine laws given to the Churches about the Control of Conception?

I answer—None.

The Churches, old and wise, gave suitable advice on sex matters in the early days, and now, confusing their own ancient wisdom with the very word of God, they give to-day similar advice, which is no longer wise.

In respect of the control of conception and general guidance concerning sex unions, the so-called Christian ethic (which incidentally goes back to Genesis for its origin, see page 411 of the First Report of the Birth Rate Commission), has for long neglected some of the highest potentialities of marriage. By chaining it to a low individualism, ignorant or forgetful that "they twain shall be one flesh," and that the married pair is not merely a couple of individuals, whose individual souls may achieve perdition or salvation, the greater truth has been hidden. I maintain that a married couple is a welded pair, a higher unit, whose existence and potentialities on this planet depend largely upon the physical condition of the material body of each of the pair, and of its interplay and exchanges, which are jeopardised without the knowledge how best to control the production of children.

The insistence sometimes made in the name of Christian "morality," that the act of physical union should take place only for the procreation of children, ignores profound physical and religious truths.

On physiological, moral, and religious grounds, therefore, I advocate the restrained sacramental and rhythmic performance of the marriage rites of physical union, throughout the whole married life, as an act of supreme value in itself, separate and distinct from its value as a basis for the procreation of children.

That being so, some knowledge of scientific methods of controlling conception becomes not only useful but of the highest—even of religious—significance.

Consider what is entailed in calling forth into existence new souls, each immortal, as all Churches maintain. This is surely one of the profoundest and most essential ways in which the Church can meet and guide humanity. Could any more exalted and more wonderful opportunity be given to the Churches than to see that the souls thus started upon their journeys, endowed with immortal power to serve or disserve God, should be brought forth in love and at such times as will give them every opportunity for complete human equipment?

The Churches, however, offer to serious and inquiring parents who can rear no more children only the alternatives of total and enforced abstinence, and the so-called "natural" method of consciously timing what should be a spontaneous natural impulse of love to those periods supposed to be "safe." Both these methods I condemn for general use, although they may suit some individual needs. Both thwart what is a high and God-given impulse, and in my opinion consequently both these practices are at times essentially immoral, almost as immoral as forcing sickly and unwanted children upon an unwilling mother and an overburdened world.

Marriage is a great and profound thing, and has a deep spiritual and physical significance apart from and in addition to being the basis of parenthood. And both these practices, allowed as the only means of birth control by the Churches, strike at the roots of the perfect marriage. The common folk who disobey and disregard this advice of the Churches, however wrong they are in their *methods*, are right in their deep instinct to obey God's ordinance that the twain shall be one flesh. There is, for this aspect of the subject, "A New Gospel."

The divine law on this great subject has not

yet been pronounced finally. The Churches have hitherto based their standard of social morality concerning it on human pronouncements. That being so, religious people should welcome the human understanding of those who to-day most seriously study the question in order to help forward the race in its material journey through space. Science, in reverent hands, may to-day on such a theme more nearly reach divine law than the Churches have yet done.

That this is being felt, even among the leaders of the Church, may be gathered from such writings as those of the Dean of St. Paul's, and the published statement by the Bishop of Birmingham (*The Times*, April 8, 1919) where he said: "Morally, as well as eugenically, it was right for people in certain circumstances to use harmless means to control the birth-rate. . . . It was immoral to avoid having children from selfish motives, but it was surely also immoral to have child after child under circumstances which, humanly speaking, were such as to render the proper upbringing of such children impossible."

Chapter III

BEFORE entering into the exact structural and medical details of the material methods advisable for those who wish to control the birth of their children, I should like to say a few words on the general subject in its relation to the normal life of the married pair.

I sincerely hope that those who propose to read this little book will *first* read my "Married Love," because the whole complex experience of married life is so interwoven with the sex act, and consequent children, that it is almost impossible to isolate the one thing, namely, the controlling of conception, and discuss that by itself without distorting its relation to the whole of life and appearing to lay stress on the minor details rather than on the greater themes. My object in the following pages is, in the interests both of the pair and of society, to spread what little light science has already thrown upon the subject, so that each pair may not only themselves be healthy and happy, but may bring forth children for the race, who have the best chance which that pair can give them of health and beauty and happiness. From a variety of causes our race is weakened by an appallingly high percentage of unfit weaklings and diseased individuals. It is perhaps only to be expected that the more conscientious, the more thrifty, and the more lovingly desirous to do the best for their children people are, the more do they restrict their families, in the interests both of the children they have and of the community which would otherwise be burdened by their offspring did they not themselves adequately provide for them. Those who are less conscientious, less full of forethought, and less able to provide for the children they bear, and more willing to accept public aid directly and indirectly, are more reckless in the production of large families. Of course there are many individual exceptions, but they do not affect the general tendency. These facts are most significantly borne out by the statistics of the birth-rates of different types of people. For instance, in the Census Report for 1911 (as published and analysed in 1912), we find that the total birth-rate per thousand married men under 55 years old is 162; but that the birth-rate for the upper and educated classes on this basis is only 119, while that of comparatively unskilled workmen is 213 and over. The detailed analysis of trades and occupations is most interesting, and should be read in conjunction with a memory of the wages and social environment of the various homes. Reckoning per thousand married men below 55 years old, the average number of children is as follows :—

Anglican clergy	101
Other ministers of religion ...	96
Teachers, professors, etc. ...	95
Doctors	103
Authors, editors, etc.	104
Policemen	153
Postmen	159
Carmen	207
Dock labourers	231
Barmen	234
Miners	258
" General labourers"	438

The above figures apply only to children born of average married people; when the vicious and feeble-minded people reproduce, they do so more recklessly.

It is found, in short, that the *numbers* of our population increasingly tend to be made up from the less thrifty and the less conscientious. Were this only a superficial matter, it would concern the race but little, but it is penetratingly profound and far-reaching. The thriftless who breed so rapidly tend by that very fact to bring forth children who are weakened and handicapped by physical as well as mental warping and weakness, and at the same time to demand their support from the sound and thrifty. It is indeed most serious for any race when (as was pointed out in 1918 in *The Times*, of the British then) less than half the population is "physically fit," even when fitness is judged by the comparatively low standard of present-day needs. Moreover we must remember that this half is not free and untrammelled, but is burdened by the partial support and upkeep of the unfit portion of the population, and hence is less able to support children of its own good type than it would be were the incapables non-existent. Hence only children with the chance of attaining strong, beautiful and intelligent maturity should be conceived. This can only be when the whole relation of each married pair is rightly adjusted, and therefore it is my earnest request that those who have not yet read "Married Love" will lay this book aside until they have done so.

. . . . .

Certain details concerning the structure of our bodies must be particularly considered in connection with the control of conception. It is possible to imagine very highly-specialised human beings who would only unite when they definitely desired a child. There are human beings to-day who advocate that course and who either practise it or endeavour to practise it, but as a race we have not evolved on lines to allow such procedure; and whether these people realise it or not, with few exceptions, they wrong their partner, they wrong themselves, and they wrong the community in which they live, by ignoring other facts and laying too heavy a burden on their own shoulders. One of the least serious, but most annoying, results to the community is a harshness of judgment, an irritableness and a tendency to quarrel and bicker, which such people frequently develop. A wise moderation should be exercised.

Our bodies bear the impress of many past material phases of our evolution; and because in the past myriads of young were needed by any race that should evolve, we still produce a far larger number of germs awaiting fertilisation than can ever be fructified and imbued with individual life. Yet each of those germs, unaware of its own futility if it reaches fertilisation at an unpropitious moment, is just as insistent in its development as the rarer favoured one which follows out the natural course of its career and gives rise to an individual. In each sex act myriads of sperm cells (each of which, had it had the female egg cell to fuse with, might have produced a living child) are daily destroyed, because in general the female has but one egg cell at a time ready for fertilisation. Control of conception consists in shutting away all the millions of sperm from the one egg, instead of allowing one of those millions to develop while all the rest of the myriads perish.

When should such steps be taken?

(*a*) After the birth of a child it is essential that there should be no hurried beginning of a second. *At least* a year should be given to the mother to regain her strength and to devote herself to the baby before a second child is conceived, preferably more than one year, and some distinguished gynæcologists even advocate as much as three or more years between births of successive children.

(*b*) In all cases of serious inherited disease, such as insanity and epilepsy, also where one or both of the partners are drunkards.

(*c*) In all cases where either of the pair is suffering from venereal disease. (It should be recognised that all sex unions at such a time are to be most strongly deprecated.)

(*d*) In all cases where for a variety of reasons all the older children are puny and utterly unsatisfactory.

(*e*) In all cases where another child coming will rob those already born of the necessary food, or will force the mother to half-starve herself to bear or rear it.

(*f*) In all cases where the mother has already had six children, *unless* she has exceptional vitality and the ardent wish to bear more. If she has the capacity and the wish to bear more children and those she already has are healthy and intelligent, then she will be doing useful work by bearing and rearing a large family.

(*g*) It is, in my opinion, advisable not to conceive a child in the very early days of marriage, because in the first few months at any rate the woman's system should be adjusting itself to new conditions, benefiting from the change in her life, and gaining poise and strength for the burden which she will have to bear. Nevertheless, some people feel that a child conceived in the first glow of rapturous union may be more precious than one born later. There is a certain cynicism about this last view, however, which I deplore, because a rightly mated and wisely temperate pair do not lose the rapture of their early love, but retain it with an added depth.

The community needs a variety of characteristics, and it is good that there should be men and women in social life who have been reared in large families, where they early gained characteristics of great service to those who fill a variety of offices. On the other hand, the children of small families, who have perhaps had more intimate affection showered upon them, also have their valuable characteristics. The human race has not yet sufficiently studied itself to have discovered more than a few mistaken ideas concerning the varying characteristics of children from small and from large families. The subject is one of very great interest, and requires intelligent handling by someone not blindly hypnotised by superficial statistics, but capable of analysing the essential factors in each life-history.

In the rough and haphazard way in which we are at present accustomed to speak about such subjects, all we can say is that where two married people have health and this world's goods sufficient to endow half a dozen or more children with health, happiness, and a good start in life, their large family is one that should be of great service to the State. Nevertheless, this should not be put before the country unthinkingly as a universal ideal. The strain of bearing more than a few children is detrimental to a large number of the best women, and this finds its expression also in weakness, a tendency to ill-health, if not actually death, on the part of their infants.

Dr. Ploetz found that nearly 60 per cent. of babies born to women who had as many as twelve children always died. When the chances of death of an infant are 60 per cent. there must surely be some very special personal reason for a woman to bear such a problematical life. Country women of robust frame, and with plenty of wholesome food and fresh air, may bear a dozen or more splendid children, but poor mothers in the crowded cities can seldom, without disaster, bring forth more than half that number.

Now it must not be imagined that by controlling births the pair are necessarily reducing the number of children they bring to maturity. As a matter of fact, by taking care to produce children only when they are fit to do so, parents immensely increase the chances of those children reaching maturity and living healthy and happy lives. It is important to notice that Holland, the country in Europe (until the war scare) the most advanced in relation to birth control, where almost everyone takes care that the children shall be well and voluntarily conceived, has greatly *increased its survival-rate*. It has the lowest infant mortality in Europe, and it has saved itself the cost and wastage of innumerable babies' coffins, while actually accelerating its rate of increase of population. America, on the other hand, where the outrageous "Comstock" laws confuse wise scientific control with illegal abortion of lives already begun and labels them both as obscene, has, by thus preventing people from obtaining decent hygienic knowledge, fostered criminal and illicit operations. Women, driven to despair, to madness, by the incessant horror of pregnancies they dread, will by hook or by crook, from the street corner or the gutter, find out how to strangle the life which should never have begun.

In my book "Married Love," in the chapter on "Children," I said, concerning the control of conception :—

. . . . .

This may be done either by shutting the sperms away from the opening of the womb or by securing the death of *all* (instead of the death of all but *one*) of the two to six hundred million sperms which enter the womb. Even when a child is allowed to grow in its mother, all these hundreds of millions of sperms are inevitably and naturally destroyed every time the man has an emission, and to add one more to these millions sacrificed by Nature is surely no crime. To kill quickly the ejaculated sperms which would otherwise die and decompose naturally is a simple matter. Their minute and uncovered bodies are plasmolised in weak acid, such as vinegar and water, or by a solution of quinine, or by many other substances.

To those who protest that we have no right to interfere with the course of Nature, one must point out that the whole of civilisation, everything which separates men from animals, is an interference with what such people commonly call Nature.

Nothing in the cosmos could be against Nature, for it all forms part of the great processes of the universe.

Actions differ, however, in their relative positions in the scale of things. Only those actions are worthy which lead the race always to a higher and fuller completion and the perfecting of its powers, which steer the race into the main current of that stream of life and vitality which courses through us and impels us forward.

It is a sacred duty of all who dare to hand on the awe-inspiring gift of life, to hand it on in a vessel as fit and perfect as they can fashion, so that the body may be the strongest and most beautiful instrument possible in the service of the soul they summon to play its part in the mystery of material being.

The exact methods I recommend are described in the next chapter.

Chapter IV

Methods Recommended

TO be entirely satisfactory a method should combine at least three essentials —safety, entire harmlessness, and the minimum disturbance of spontaneity in the sex act (that is to say, it should be as little inæsthetic as is possible).

Marriage is too often the grave of romance, and undoubtedly the disabilities of recurrent pregnancies, and the consequent necessity which married people have so long felt of using some means of prevention, have done much to deaden the beauty and undermine the security of the marriage relation. Alas! that it should be so, but without question many of the less worthy people have known better how to retain the adventitious charms of union than have those united in holy wedlock.

Ideally all knowledge of methods of controlling conception should be confined to the married and those immediately about to marry. Something approaching a sacred initiation into the rites of marriage should be available, under dignified and impressive circumstances, for every wedded pair, but alas! this is a remote ideal, and to-day far too often the married are in ignorance of what should most vitally concern them.

This book is written essentially for the married. It is true that it may pass, directly or indirectly, into the hands of those who have not put any religious or civil seal on the bond of their love. But if it does, one can be sure that it will reduce, and not increase, the racial dangers which are so often coincident with illicit love. Moreover, as I have often said on the public platform when questioned about the dangers of spreading immorality, the methods which I advise and those disseminated by the Clinic and the Society for Constructive Birth Control *cannot be used by a virgin girl.* While on the other hand, if the knowledge in this book may enable a few wives *apparently* without reason to avoid all childbearing, it is surely well that such women should not be mothers, for motherhood is too sacred an office to be held unwillingly.

Some people, generally those who have been brought up in the hazy ignorance of either an idealistic or a shamefaced attitude towards sex, refuse to use any preventive method. Not infrequently a woman who has had several children and acquired a fear of pregnancy so refuses, and cuts off her husband from all normal intercourse, with, possibly, serious effects on the health of both. Such people should try to realise that because there may be a few inartistic moments in a course of procedure, that cannot rationally be held to prohibit the procedure. It would be as reasonable to decide that as some of the processes of cooking and the after-effects of digestion are inartistic, solid food should not be taken. In this physical world we are to a considerable extent dependent on the physical facts of our bodies, which we cannot override without making grievous trouble either for ourselves or those around us.

No method is *absolutely* safe, but if two methods, each very nearly reliable, are combined, then something approaching absolute safety is achieved. It must be remembered, however, that the most perfect procedure devisable cannot be safe in the hands of one who is careless. The one to whom the consequences of carelessness are most serious is, of course, the woman; she, therefore, is the one who should exercise the precaution. Consequently she must have knowledge sufficient to be sure that she is taking the right steps. A large number of women are not acquainted with the physical structure of the human body; it is, therefore, necessary to describe a few essential features which all women must understand in order to take the best precautions.

A married woman has no difficulty in distinguishing the entrance of the vagina. The vagina itself is not a sex organ, but is the canal leading to the important internal organ—the womb. The ovaries, the actual source of the egg cells, are entirely internal and do not con-

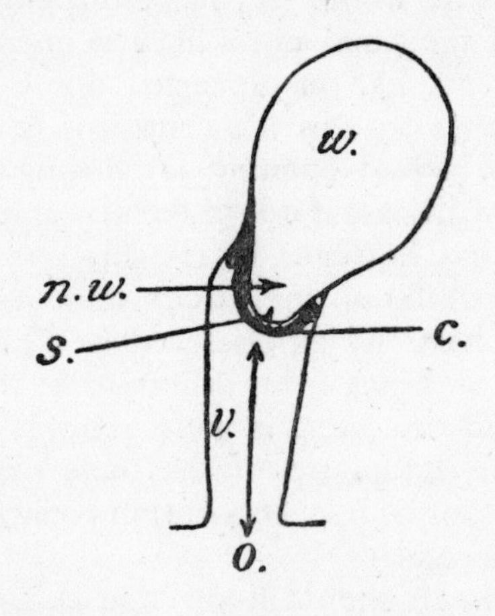

cern us here. The womb, however, though it is internal, can readily be felt near the end of the vaginal canal (*v* in diagram) if the woman feels for it with her longest finger (of which the nail should be very clean, and is best covered with boracic vaseline before it is gently inserted). The distance from the opening of the vaginal orifice (*o*), which is the external opening, to the end of the vaginal canal where the womb can be just felt by most women, is generally about the length of the woman's own finger, although some women are made with long vaginal canals and short fingers; just as some have long noses and short chins. Such women may find it difficult to use this particular method; they are relatively few in number however. The womb (*w*) lies internally, but at the end of the canal and a little to one side, its neck projects like an inverted dome of soft firm tissue (*n w*); in the centre of this is the very small actual opening (*s*) through which the sperm will pass if it is to fertilise an egg cell. This opening, however, is very small, and would not be felt under normal circumstances by most women. I have myself observed, and have confirmatory evidence from others, that there are times when this neck is wide enough open to receive the actual tip of the male organ. At such times, of course, conception is particularly likely to take place.

The woman should know that this opening is there, and that, therefore, if she wishes to prevent the sperm reaching the ovum this small entrance is the critical gateway through which the sperm must not be permitted to pass. In the vagina itself the sperms are merely waiting in the ante-room. The vagina, however, is of great importance to the man in the sex act, for it is into the vagina that his organ enters, and there it receives the sensations necessary for the completion of the normal act, the contact of the soft tissues of the parts being an important element in the right performance of the vital function. The ideal preventive method, therefore, does not interpose anything between the tissues of the vaginal canal and the male organ, but it should close the minute entrance of the womb and shut away the sperm from entering that critical part.

The best appliance at present available for doing this is a small rubber cap, made on a firm rubber ring, which is accurately fixed round the dome-like end of the womb. It adheres by suction assisted by the resilience of the firm rim against the circular muscles and remains securely in place, whatever movement the woman may make. They do not grip or pinch the neck of the womb, as is often implied by ignorant critics of the method. (In the diagram, *c* shows the rubber cap in position.) These small rubber caps are quite simple, strong, easily fitted, and should be procurable from any first-class chemist.[1] The important point about adjusting them is that they should be of the right size. The average woman is fitted by a small or a medium size, but the

[1] This round rubber cap is called the small check pessary or small occlusive pessary ; sometimes, incorrectly, the *small* mensinga. I am not here speaking of the larger mensinga or matrisalus pessaries. A great variety of names are given to various types of the small occlusive pessary ; the best make seems to me to be the ProRace. Forms with air-rims are often advised, but experience at the Clinic is against them. (See Appendix, pp. 79–81.)

woman who has had several children generally wants them larger. Educated and intelligent women can generally fit themselves quite easily, but some women cannot, and for them personal instruction is necessary.

Women who are quite healthy, and under the impression that they are entirely normal, may perhaps find the use of this cap impossible, or find that if they do use it, it fails them, because, without knowing it, they may have experienced some internal after-effects of child-birth. One of the commonest (which is of frequent occurrence among those women who have been to the Clinic) is the laceration of the neck of the womb as a result of the stretching by the child's head at birth. The result is that, although the neck of the womb has healed, and the woman is quite unconscious of any pain or disability, instead of a circular contracting muscle, the neck consists of two or more flaps, one of which may get on the outside of the rim of the cap or otherwise interfere with its proper placing, and in any case make it difficult or unreliable for the woman to place it in position herself. Hence, unless a woman is acquainted with anatomy and *knows* herself to be normal, it is much better that she should be examined by an expert, such as the nurse at our Clinic or one of the doctors in touch with our Clinic, before using the cap herself. After one examination, a healthy woman need have no further expert assistance until she has another child, when she should be examined again after child-birth.

For women who are doubtful about their own perfect normality, or where injury has occurred during child-birth, the simpler method advised on page 52 should meanwhile be used.

Before insertion the rubber cap should be moistened with very soapy water, so as to allow it to slip in easily. Quinine ointment is sometimes preferred for this purpose, and if both the inside and outside of the cap be well covered with it, it may be unnecessary to insert a quinine pessary later (see page 41) if the cap is very well fitted. It should be placed in its position for use at any convenient time, preferably when dressing in the evening and some hours before going to bed. The great advantage of this cap is that once it is in and firmly and properly fitted it can be entirely forgotten, and neither the man nor the woman can detect its presence. This point, although primarily an æsthetic and emotional one, is of supreme physiological benefit also, and is one of the strongest arguments for this method. The cap should be put in at least some hours before bedtime, and left in undisturbed until *at least* the following day; but I very much advise it being left in two or three days after any individual act of union. The reason for this will be mentioned below. After use, even if the cap is to be again inserted in an hour or two, it should be carefully washed in soapy water, and though not essential where there is perfect health, it is much better to dip it into a weak solution of some wholesome disinfectant before putting it away in the jar of water recommended in the Appendix. Some women, as advised by the medical man who invented caps, insert the cap when the monthly period has entirely ceased, and leave it in for three weeks, but I have never recommended this and consider it inadvisable. This is safe only with *perfect* health, and few of our modern women can boast that. The cap should not be worn needlessly: there is no reason to do so, as it can be slipped in easily when desired. If a woman suffers even trifling ill-health, accompanied by a slight local discharge, then there is no doubt that the cap should never be left in more than a couple of days at a time, though after being taken out for an hour or two and cleansed, it may be re-inserted on the same day. A woman who needs to use her cap very frequently would do well to have two and to keep them alternately in a disinfectant solution. Women very greatly vary in their vaginal effect on rubber. When it is unlikely that it will be required, it is always better *not* to keep the cap in place but to remove it.

Now the cap alone, if it really fits and if it

is left in for two days so that the sperm are naturally got rid of without having a chance to enter, should be completely safe by itself. There is, however, always the possibility of a slight displacement or of a particularly active sperm remaining after the cap has been taken out and then using the opportunity to swim into the entrance of the womb. To render this impossible, or at any rate unlikely in the extreme, it is as well to plasmolise the sperms when they first come in; and in order to do this the best method is to have some plasmolising substance in the vagina at the time when the sperms are deposited. The reason why it is better to do this rather than to wait and deal with the sperms afterwards is given in the paragraph on douching (see page 66).

Several substances may be used for the purpose of plasmolising the sperms. One which is very easy, and widely used because it is specially prepared and can be purchased readily, is the soluble quinine pessary. This is a mixture of various quinine compounds with cocoa-butter for its greasy base. In my opinion the grease affords valuable protection, and the same quinine compounds mixed with gelatine or other non-greasy substances (sometimes sold to those who object to grease) are not as reliable. Experience at the Clinic, however, has confirmed what I knew from personal experience many years ago, namely, that quinine is partly absorbed by the vaginal walls and does not entirely suit all women. We have had prepared for use at the Clinic (and have there tested them) greasy suppositories made entirely without quinine, and with chinosol in its place. Chinosol is a harmless and very satisfactory disinfectant, specially recommended by Sir Arbuthnot Lane for its valuable properties. Hence, for a double reason, the chinosol greasy pessary is to be preferred to the quinine, for while the quinine pessary is satisfactory to about 95 per cent. of women, the chinosol pessary is completely satisfactory, and the chinosol has a subsidiary useful property. Since it has been perfected, it has been the only form of greasy pessary recommended at the Clinic. Like the greasy quinine pessary, it can be slipped in at the last few moments, so that the crisis is not æsthetically interfered with.

In a few words, therefore, I advise as the safest and readiest method of contraception for the perfectly normal woman, that she should use the all-rubber cap fitted in some time before retiring, and slip the chinosol greasy pessary in a few minutes before the act. With these precautions, nothing further need be done. There is no getting up to douche or to take other precautions in the middle of the night. It is not even necessary to remove the cap or to take any steps the following morning. The usual processes of Nature will dispose of the now impotent sperms. Those who are very anxious, however, who may feel this calm inactivity insufficient, may desire to douche the next morning and take out the cap. If they wish to do so, there is no harm in using one of the douches mentioned on page 71, so long as douching is not too frequently indulged in and does not become a regular habit.

The action of quinine on the vagina varies considerably with different types of women. For the average woman it is quite harmless, and indeed for some beneficial. More detail about this interesting point will be found in my larger text-book, "Contraception, Its Theory and Practice." On the other hand, I am convinced that it is, at least, partly absorbed by the walls of the vaginal canal, and thus penetrates the system in such a way as to make peculiarly sensitive women either somewhat sleepless or to interfere slightly with the digestion, or to initiate local tenderness. It has been proved by scientific experiment that some substances (iodine, for instance) do penetrate through the walls of the vagina and get into the circulatory system with remarkable rapidity. Whether or not the same applies to quinine has never been tested, so far as I am aware, except by the actual experience of those who have long used it as a contraceptive. I am satisfied that it does penetrate the system of some (and therefore presumably of all) women; thereupon it depends on the individual's general reactions whether it is beneficial or upsetting. Women who have for some time past used quinine pessaries have no need to feel doubtful about them or to stop their usage if they are entirely satisfied with them; but those beginning the use of contraceptives would be better advised to use chinosol greasy pessaries from the first.

One slight drawback to any soluble greasy pessary is that the cocoa-butter, of which they are made, has a smell to which some people object; but this is now almost universally overcome by the various makers who have placed on the market odourless or pleasantly scented cocoa-butter pessaries.

A slight disadvantage of the greasy pessary when made in the ordinary size is that it produces more lubrication than is necessary for some women, and the friction, essential for the complete orgasm, may be difficult to obtain. Such people should use the small-sized chinosol pessary which is now obtainable.

The only real drawback to a greasy pessary is that the melted cocoa-butter tends to spread on to linen. For those who object to this or find it inconvenient in any way, the following suggestions may be useful as alternatives:—

(*a*) A pad of cotton wool, thoroughly smeared with vaseline, which has been mixed with powdered borax, may be inserted into the end of the vagina. This may be used by those who find soap in any way unpleasant, or irritating, as it should tend to be more soothing.

(*b*) A strip of boracic lint may be inserted and packed round the cap after its insertion and not very long before union takes place. This is perhaps the cleanest and easiest of these alternatives.

None of these methods, however, seem to me so easy nor quite so satisfactory as the soluble greasy pessary.

Several varieties of soluble pessaries are made with other substances on the Continent, but they are not so easily obtained in this country, though some, particularly of German make, are being pushed. In France the peasant women make up such things for themselves, and a woman who has time and skill could do this, using gelatine instead of cocoa-butter. Gelatine, however, is not in itself an assistance, as is cocoa-butter, and so gelatine suppositories are less reliable than ones composed of a greasy substance. The grease itself clogs the sperms and prevents their movements.

The greatest care should be exercised in getting a rubber cap exactly to fit. In order to put it in, the woman should be in a stooping position, sitting on her heels with her knees completely bent, and she should press the rim of the cap together so as to slip it into the opening. When the cap reaches the end of the vaginal canal it will naturally expand and then tends to find its place itself (*c* in diagram). It wants pressing firmly round the protuberance of the womb, however, and if it is too small it may miss covering the critical opening. It should be the largest size which fits with comfort, and the rounded neck of the womb should be felt in the soft part of the cap. One too large, of course, will leave a gap and be more disastrous than one too small. A woman who is afraid of her own body or ignorant of her own physiology should get a practitioner to fit her with a rubber cap or attend the Birth Control Clinic; but for women of average intelligence this is not necessary. (It is shown in place in the diagram at *c*.) On the other hand, as the relative sizes of all the parts of our bodies vary very much, a woman may have a vaginal canal longer than her own centre finger, and would then have to be fitted by a medical practitioner, a nurse, or some competent person. In the first instance, she should purchase more than one size to find out exactly what suits her. On each occasion it should be pressed firmly, after some active movement, to see that it does not slip. When the cap is once firmly on, both the man and the woman can be at ease about it, as it should remain in a couple of days without dislodgment. But it should be tested by feeling round it before each time of union. It should perhaps be mentioned that it is quite impossible for the cap to enter farther or get into the body cavity and "lose itself" among the organs, as some ignorant people fear.

In order to get it out, all that is necessary is to bend a finger under its rim and jerk it off. The cap can then be brought out, washed and left to dry until it is next wanted. The little jerk at the edge of the rim itself is necessary to overcome the suction effect, which some women find unpleasant when they merely tug at the ribbon which is generally attached to the rim of the cap and lies along the vagina when the cap is in place. It is generally better to have a cap without any such attachment, or to cut off this ribbon and its attachment and rely solely on the finger to jerk off the cap. Rubber tends to rot; so, after some months' use, it should be carefully examined to see that it is not torn or become liable to be readily perforated. If the woman can afford it, I should recommend a new one every six months or so, though with great care they will last a couple of years.

A great many different forms of rubber cap are on the market, shaped in various ways, but the circular, strong ring, with the high dome-shaped soft centre, called the ProRace, is the kind I recommend and which to the average woman is by far the most satisfactory. The rim should be composed of firm and solid, but soft and flexible, rubber, and *not* contain any metal spring or wire. (See Appendix.)

This procedure on the part of the woman, though it may sound elaborate and a little sordid when described in full detail, is, nevertheless, after the first usage, so simple and so unobtrusive, that it can be entirely forgotten during the marriage rite itself. It therefore alone among mechanical preventive methods does not tend to destroy the sense of spontaneous and uninterrupted feeling, which is so vital an element in the perfected union, and at the same time allows all the benefit to be derived from it. Doubtless when once the intelligent inquiry and scientific research commensurate with the importance of the subject are devoted to it, better preventive methods may be devised, although there seems little immediate prospect of any more satisfactory new method meeting *all* the requirements. In the meantime this combination of methods is far the best course which is available at present, and, indeed, the only one which I can sincerely recommend, and it has the endorsement of the leading medical practitioners.

. . . . .

A medical practitioner opposed to contraception has announced that he has known women who cannot wear the cap I describe, quoting one lady doctor even as being unable to insert the cap for herself: from this he implied that the cap must therefore be useless! His argument was absurd, for he was quoting cases which are abnormal in a scientific sense, and applying the result to the normal. I think I know personally the lady doctor to whom he refers; but at any rate I know *a* lady doctor who consulted me and told me she could not fix the cap as she has a very long vagina and small hands. In quite early editions of this book I noted such exceptions (and others) who would be unable to wear the cap. The opponent who uses them in argument against the method for *normal* women is only arguing illogically and should not be allowed to influence reasonable opinion.

. . . . .

Another medical practitioner, in favour of contraception, Mr. Norman Haire, M.B., has recently (July, 1922, in the Malthusian League's practical leaflet) advocated the Dutch or hemispherical type of cap in preference to the small occlusive I describe above. I welcome the fact that the other Society should now adopt my main thesis, namely that an internal rubber cap worn by the woman is the best form of contraception. Whether one shape of cap or another is worn is a point of minor difference, as the *fundamental* principle is the same in the use of all the various internal rubber caps, though they vary greatly in details. Most unfortunately Mr. Haire ardently advocates the Dutch simple half-sphere pessary in preference to the small occlusive cap worn on the neck of the womb. I wish therefore to point out serious objections to the Dutch cap which its masculine advocates entirely overlook.[1] Since stating these objections in the *Lancet* further serious drawbacks to this type of cap have come to my notice.

The Dutch cap must be worn so as to cover the whole end of the vagina, and it is therefore necessary for a woman to wear a cap with a very much larger diameter than would be the diameter of the occlusive pessary, for the Dutch cap depends on a certain *stretching* of the end of the vaginal walls for its power to remain in position. Hence the user of the Dutch cap has the end of the vagina stretched, and moreover the end of the vagina is stretched in such a way that certain movements of physiological value which ideally the woman should make are then impossible. It is true that few women either know or practise the completest physiological and natural union; but, in my opinion, that is no reason for justifying the advocacy of a means of contraception which inherently makes certain natural and valuable movements impossible.

[1] See also my letter in the *Lancet* September 9, 1922, p. 588.

A further objection to the Dutch cap is that, of necessity, it must cover the whole end of the vagina, and that therefore the tissues immediately round the neck of the womb are deprived of contact with the seminal fluid. There is reason to believe that these tissues are among the most sensitive as well as most absorptive of the woman; they are not covered or interfered with by the small occlusive cap with narrow rim which I advise, but they are completely covered by the Dutch cap, and it is *not* good that they should be covered.

I am therefore opposed to the use of the Dutch or Malthusian cap advocated by Mr. Haire for general use.

At my Clinic we have advised the Dutch cap now and then for abnormal or difficult cases, when it sometimes proves very useful. Cases, for instance, when the woman has become excessively fat and the internal organs are stretched or out of place, and she is therefore incapable of the ideal and perfect movement anyway, and finds it difficult or impossible to adjust the small cap; also cases when the neck of the womb is injured, and some others.

But throughout all my work on behalf of our sex-life, I only *advocate* procedure for the normal and healthy, in the hope that they may improve and make more perfect their own lives. I recognise as useful palliatives or as necessary treatment a great variety of measures suitable for the great variety of diseased, injured and abnormal persons now among us; but I deplore the tendency still rampant to set our general standards by such persons. The advocacy of the Dutch cap for *general* use by a medical practitioner is only one more regrettable illustration of the all-too-frequent fact that the medical profession (consisting of those who treat *disease*) is frequently blind to the requirements, to the existence even, of perfect and joyous *health*.

SPONGE AND OIL METHOD

As mentioned on page 38, some women have a lacerated cervix without in any other way suffering in their health, and some have slight prolapse or other defect sufficient to make the fitting of a cap difficult or unreliable. Some find the actual fixing of the cap beyond their unaided powers. For these and other reasons the cap is not always suitable for use by those who cannot have expert personal advice, and for a long time past I have recommended to women unable immediately to get the necessary examination and help that they should meanwhile utilise the recent modification of an old-fashioned method which we are finding satisfactory at the Clinic. This is the original "sponge method," first publicly made known in this country in 1823, and now generally superseded by more elaborate and expensive things.

We find, particularly in homes where life is simple and the desire is to spend little money, that the simplest, safest and easiest method for uninstructed women to use is to soak in olive oil a fine-grained sponge (rounded to about the size of a small orange, and selected with care so that no large holes penetrate it). It should be soaked well in olive oil (or ordinary salad oil), and the oil nearly all squeezed out before the sponge is inserted. Some prefer olive oil with chinosol dissolved in it.

Some years ago, when this book was first written, a large proportion of the women of the country who were healthy and normal turned to it for contraceptive information; now the greater number of normal and intelligent women are satisfied and have got information which they are using; but what may be described as the "difficult cases" are still trying one type of contraceptive after another, seeking one to suit them. The increasing proportion of difficult cases coming to the Clinic [1] shows that the study of contraceptives must reach a stage when the injured, abnormal or difficult case must be specially considered. Meanwhile I recommend the use of the sponge soaked in oil as most likely to succeed with slightly injured or somewhat difficult cases, for, although the cap is simplicity itself to adjust when used by

[1] See "The First Five Thousand," by Dr. Marie Stopes. Published by Bale, Sons and Danielsson, Ltd., London.

a *normal* woman, it is not entirely suitable for the abnormal or injured, or those very ignorant and inexperienced.

I should like to emphasise the very important fact that contraception for *normal* women is the simplest possible *hygienic* measure; but contraception for the injured or abnormal, even in a slight degree, may be a complicated and difficult *medical* problem.

. . . . .

The most difficult cases of all, and at the same time those most urgently needing to exert reliable control over conception, are the women who are harried, overworked and worried into a dull and careless apathy. These too often will not, or cannot, take the care and trouble to adjust ordinary methods of control so as to secure themselves from undesirable conceptions. Yet they do not desire more children, and often have already produced a number of low-grade or semi-feeble-minded puny infants.

All health workers, district nurses, and workers in schools for mothers know scores of such women, and many have appealed to me asking what they are to advise for women too careless to use any ordinary method and yet who continue to give birth to hopelessly inferior infants which are only an expense and drag upon the community.

For such, in some of the former editions of

this book, I suggested a method which leading American medicals have used with advantage, but I have found that the technique which is required is not yet sufficiently familiar to practitioners in this country to make it readily available. I trust the interest now taken in the matter may lead to a speedy recognition of the value of the lead given us in this direction by practitioners of other countries.

It seems easy enough to supply the intelligent and careful woman with physiological help ; and for the careless, stupid or feeble-minded who persist in producing infants of no value to the State and often only a charge upon it, the right course seems to be sterilisation.

STERILISATION

Curiously enough, in this country sterilisation is considered more mysterious and more feared than in America, where a number of States have compulsory sterilisation laws, and where thousands of sterilisations have been carried out successfully.

It ought to be known in this country that there is at present no quite simple and satisfactory method of sterilising women. Hence just the type of woman who most certainly should be sterilised in the interests of the State and of herself, namely, one with a slightly subnormal mentality or liable to epileptic fits, drink, etc., cannot be successfully sterilised without a major operation, so that she must use most carefully birth control methods or refrain entirely from married life.

But for men, sterilisation is comparatively easy—so trifling an operation that it is described by a leading American medical man as "an office operation" when it is performed by simple vasectomy (see *Birth Control News*, June, 1923, Vol. II, No. 2). Of course, this is well known to medical practitioners, many of whom would be quite willing to perform the operation on their patients for moderate fees if they were requested to do so, but they shrink from suggesting it. It is for the public to take the matter into their own hands and ask for sterilisation for themselves or their children where it should be done. For instance, boys should be sterilised in families where there is epilepsy, or any degree of feeble-mindedness, not only in the parents but in the collaterals such as uncles or aunts, for feeble-mindedness and epilepsy are apt to "miss a generation," and appear in a manner unexpected to the parents, although the likelihood of the calamity arising is obvious to scientists who know some of the laws which govern these deplorable racial defects. Now that birth control is becoming so well established, it is time that the idea of sterilisation should be familiarised, so that those who would benefit by its application to themselves or their own families should be free without fear or anxiety to utilise it. The public will be ready to utilise it for racial purposes when its urgent need is realised. Not long ago a letter in *The Times* signed by some distinguished medical men advocated sterilisation in this country.

There are great varieties of individual needs on the part of various people, and as a good many other methods are in common use a few words about them are necessary, as I find that many people are using them without realising that they may thereby, to a greater or less degree, injure themselves.

Chapter V

Comments on and Objections to a Few of the Important Methods in Use

THE SHEATH

THE shutting away of the sperm from the womb can be as completely achieved by covering the male organ as it can by covering the mouth of the womb by the rubber cap, as has just been described. This method is perhaps the best known of all in current use, and *sheaths* under various names, formed either from rubber, skin, or treated silk, are sold in a variety of qualities and designs. They are alike, however, in the essential, namely, that they enclose the male organ, completely preventing the sperm from escaping into the vagina.

These are certainly among the most "harmless" of the methods recommended by many people, and, where a pair has used them with satisfaction, there is no essential need to discard them. In my opinion, however, there are objections to them which are sufficiently serious to make the use of a sheath, except under special conditions, inadvisable.

A serious objection is that the sheath prevents the seminal fluid reaching the woman, a subject I have gone into more fully in my book, "Contraception: Its Theory, History and Practice." I have maintained that there is a physiological advantage to the woman in the partial absorption of the man's secretions, which must take place through the permeable wall of the vaginal canal, quite apart from the separate and distinct act of fertilisation. If, as physiology has proved is the case, the internal absorption of secretions from the sex organs plays so large a part in determining the health and character of remote parts of the body, it is extremely likely that the highly-stimulating secretion of man's seminal fluid can and does penetrate and affect the woman's whole organism. Actual experiment has shown that iodine and other substances placed in the vagina in solution are so quickly absorbed that in less than an hour they have penetrated the system and are being excreted. Extended experience only increases my certainty of the beneficial effect of coitus, and the conviction that some subtle substances are mutually absorbed to the benefit of both parties, as they can be when the cap is used.

A further objection to the use of the sheath is that it reduces the closeness of contact and thus destroys the sense of complete union which is not only pleasurable, but is definitely soothing to the nerves and physiologically and spiritually advantageous in every way.

A minor, but nevertheless important, objection is an æsthetic one—the putting on of a sheath, the feel of its texture, and the consciousness that it is there, destroy the spontaneous beauty of what should be the natural development of mutual feeling.

If, however, *it is absolutely essential* that no risk should be run of the wife becoming pregnant (if, for instance, it would kill her to have another child), then perhaps the sheath may be used in addition to the method taken by the wife, because no one method gives *absolute* security by itself, though it may give 9,999 chances of security to one of danger. But for normal healthy people I do not recommend the sheath.

Advice is often given about washing and disinfecting the sheath so that it can be used again. But this is not really a wise procedure, for few private people are likely to be sufficiently careful to make such disinfection complete. Preferably the sheath should be destroyed and a fresh one used each time.

. . . . .

COITUS INTERRUPTUS

The method perhaps most widely in use of all, and which appeals to many people because it requires no special appliance or chemicals, is *withdrawal*, or *coitus interruptus*. Many who are inclined, without sufficient knowledge, to condemn other methods, consider that this must be entirely harmless, because nothing is involved which they consider "unnatural," and it is even miscalled self-control, and thus surrounded by an odour of approval and sanctity very misleading to those who do not probe into realities. The same misnomer is also applied to absolute continence (see page 12). Nevertheless, this method has without doubt done an incredible amount of harm, not directly, but through its reactions on the nervous systems of both man and woman. Many doctors, now that the subject has been opened, have communicated with me confirming this statement from their experience. To a medical correspondent I am indebted for the interesting observation that "coitus interruptus" is not a certain method of controlling conception, owing to the presence of active sperm cells in the beads of clear secretion which are often present on the male organ during erection and *before* ejaculation has taken place. This doctor has seen under the microscope in his own case active sperm in such drops. This fact may be the reason behind those fairly frequent cases where undesired conception has taken place and both parties unite in declaring that none of the ejaculation touched the woman. There are a few arguments in favour of withdrawal which make some people regret its condemnation, the chief of these arguments being that it requires no outlay of money and that it is available at any time and place. Individuals who have particularly strong muscular and nervous systems may go through life using this method and feel from it no ill-effects. Their advocacy, however, should not blind the greater number of people to its dangers. Some men are strong enough to feel no evil effects even from its constant practice; but others who do not trace it directly to this are, nevertheless, sufferers through their nerves, and consequently through their digestions and power of sleep (ills which a competent observer can trace to this procedure); and some men are acutely conscious of its ill-effects.

The great majority of women whose husbands practise this method suffer very fundamentally as a result of the reiterated stirring-up of local nervous excitement which is deprived of its natural physiological resolution. Of the far-reaching effects on the woman's entire organism of the lack of a proper orgasm, which is generally a result of this method, this is not the place to speak, and the reader is referred to "Married Love," where various aspects of the subject are more fully considered. Some women whose husbands are among those capable of using this method without apparent ill-effect, maintain that the husband can, and always should, control his reaction sufficiently long to give the wife her complete orgasm before his withdrawal. Such power on the part of the average man, however, does not seem very common. Where it exists, it does undoubtedly remove the objection to withdrawal indicated in the preceding passage, but even in the best of circumstances the following specific objections exist. The local support and nerve-soothing contact which are supplied mutually to both when the act is completed normally are destroyed. The man, instead of allowing himself the normal ease and relaxation of attention which should be the concomitant of the act, has to keep a strain upon his attention in order to withdraw at exactly the right second; he is thus straining not only his local nervous system, but his central nervous system.

The woman, even when she has the good fortune to have a husband with exceptional powers of control, is always in a state of anxiety in case the withdrawal should not be rightly timed, or that some of the fluid should accidentally touch her. In either case pregnancy is possible; so that *her* central system, as well as her local nervous system, is also strained. The act, therefore, cannot have the soothing and healing power which it normally should have, and is, moreover, resolved into its lowest terms—merely physical "relief" for the man.

In addition to this, if there is the slightest delay in withdrawal or any carelessness, the woman has immediately to arise from the warm bed and douche, in the anxious hope that she may be in time. (Concerning douching, see what I have to say below, p. 66.)

Except for cases of emergency or in circumstances involving accidental lack of other means, or by exceptional people who have become specially adapted to this malpractice, withdrawal should never be used. Most unfortunately, by a certain "virtuous" type of person this method is described as "self-restraint," and so has been surrounded with an aura of approval, and thus the incalculable harm it does is increased.

Another practice which is sometimes advocated as a method of control of conception is in some ways a further extension of the power to withdraw at will. It is, in truth, a real form of self-restraint, though it is not the restraint of abstinence from all connection. This method consists in a strong mental control exerted by the man after his entry, a control which differs from that in the practice of withdrawal in that it aims at avoiding any ejaculation whatsoever, while at the same time retaining erection and remaining as long as possible in the closest union with the beloved. This controlled restraint appears to be possible to a certain type of man, and it has been studied and has formed the subject both of experiment and published statements for nearly a century. The mental attitude of those who adopt it can be essentially summed up in a few words: Union for the mutual spiritual and physical sense of joy and comradeship, kept distinct from the procreative act by the strongest possible guidance and control by the will, so that the procreative act or ejaculation does not take place at all. Those who practise this method speak with enthusiasm in its favour. I find, however, most medical men in this country, who are cognisant of it, are very strongly against it, and from general deductions I think it is safe to assume that it is not particularly suited to the average Englishman's temperament and powers, and indeed might very well be detrimental to his health. Although this book is essentially addressed to the average, the advanced and the more spiritually minded as well as the "intellectual" and under-sexed types should not be ignored, and for all such there is no doubt that this method would *appear* to avoid many of the drawbacks and objections to mechanical methods of preventing conception. Though I must disclaim any expression of opinion in its favour, if it proves valuable and health-giving to some and highly detrimental to others, data collected on this point may throw light on still further fundamental divergencies in human needs and construction, and be of great social interest and value.

. . . . .

METAL INSTRUMENTS

Various instruments, some of metal, have been made and from time to time recommended for the internal use of women. They should in any circumstance only be used after the fullest and most competent medical examination and must be fitted by a doctor. For some unfortunate women who have been damaged by child-birth, and whose organs are no longer normally placed, they may be necessary. For normal women they are generally to be condemned.

. . . . .

DOUCHING

The method most widely practised by women, and which is recommended as not only "harmless" but by many as positively beneficial, is *douching*. About this method there is much to say.

In the first place, in the nature of things the douching must come *after* the act of union. As sometimes the sperm may be ejected actually into the womb itself, douching after the event may be quite futile. But even where this has not happened, and the sperms are still in the vaginal canal, it resolves itself into a race between the plasmolising fluid and the sperms; and the sperms, having already got something of a start, may win the race and penetrate the womb. In that event douching may be entirely too late. There is, therefore, no certainty whatever in the method of douching, though as a result of the shock and general discomfort entailed it may very often inhibit conception.

The objections to it, even if it were, what it is not, a safe method, are twofold: æsthetic and physiological. The æsthetic objection is by no means to be despised, for the effect both on man and wife of having immediately to rise from a warm embrace and come down to the crudest material facts of douches and chemicals at the moment when the whole relation should be one of tenderest mutual feeling and repose, is desolatingly disillusioning to a romantic man or woman. In not a few instances it has broken up sex relations entirely by destroying the man's sense of romance, so that he is no longer capable of physically loving his wife, while there are wives who refuse all sex relations to their husbands on the ground that the douching involved is intolerable.

The man, however, is often saved the disadvantages by the natural sleep which follows his completed act. It is the woman who chiefly suffers by this method. Physical reactions on the woman are of two principal kinds: the first, subtler, and generally overlooked, is that her inclination to sleep (if she has been fortunate enough to have had the completed act) is thwarted if not entirely destroyed. The tendency of this is to make her nervous, and, if she is highly strung, to induce chronic sleeplessness. On the other hand, she also suffers from the local chill of getting up out of a warm bed and moving about the room, unless she is one of the very few fortunate ones who can afford a fire in a bedroom and a maid to prepare the warm douche. Most women have to do these things themselves, and even douching with warm water does not eliminate the general chill.

There is, however, another and more serious objection against the douching which is so widely advocated. It washes out and destroys the bacterial inhabitants of the vaginal canal. People insufficiently acquainted with science have jumped to the conclusion that this is a good thing, because some bacteria are known to them to be enemies of mankind. They think it therefore an act of cleanliness to wash out the vaginal canal, and they even go so far as to compare it with brushing the teeth and rinsing the mouth.

Some people, observing the "dirty" little nodules on the root of the pea plant, and being told that they contain bacteria, would be impelled to pinch them off—thereby depriving the plant of its most valuable allies—the bacteria which "fix" the nitrogen from the air and which consequently place the pea plant in a more advantageous position than most of the members of the vegetable kingdom. It is true that doctors have not yet thoroughly examined or discovered exactly what part the bacteria in the vagina play in the internal economy of the woman, but sufficient evidence has accumulated to show the folly of destroying them and at the same time affecting the lining of the vaginal canal. For some years I had been against douching, save in emergencies, and shortly before I wrote this book a definite denunciation of douching was published in the *British Medical Journal* of April 20, 1918, by Dr. Fothergill. This article is, of course, by no means final, any more than are my own private views on the matter, but it deserves the careful attention of the many people who indulge in or recommend the frequent use of the douche of all kinds.

Nevertheless, there are occasions when douching may be necessary, and when it is only used infrequently it can do no harm if the proper solutions are used.

Regarding the solutions which should be employed when a douche seems advisable, a large number of substances, all of which are soluble or mixable with water, have been recommended by various people. It is to be remembered that at present I am recommending only those suitable for normal healthy people. Specific diseases, of course, require specific treatment.

Many of the so-called "harmless" substances used for the douche are very far from being entirely harmless. Such a chemical as corrosive sublimate, for instance, which has often been recommended, ought not to be placed in the hands of the private individual haphazard, and, moreover, though but few serious cases are on record against it, when one realises that the vaginal walls may absorb part at least of the fluid, its use is to be entirely deprecated save for specific diseases.

Lysol, carbolic acid and other such strong fluids, though "harmless" if diluted sufficiently, are, nevertheless, destructive rather than healing in their action, and if by accident used too strong, or even if used frequently by a sensitive subject, are very apt to lead to sores or even partial destruction of the tissues.

Only the simplest and most wholesome substances, therefore, are to be recommended for general use. For the purpose of douching to plasmolise the sperms, either vinegar and water or common salt and water could scarcely be bettered. If vinegar and water are used, it should be in about two parts of warm water to one of vinegar. A stronger solution would do no harm if used infrequently, but would tend to harden the vaginal walls if used regularly. Common salt should be made into a strong solution, and about two tablespoonfuls of salt to a pint of water. These solutions are quite sufficient to incapacitate any sperm, and at the same time they contain no substance in the slightest degree deleterious or even very foreign to the system if partly absorbed.

People have for too long coupled normal prevention for quite healthy people with disinfection of one or other of the pair where disease exists or is suspected. In this book I am not dealing with cases of the diseased or the medically unfit in any way. They may, under doctor's orders, have to use strong, even perhaps dangerous chemicals. I am now only advising the perfectly normal and healthy what to use to keep themselves normal and healthy, for I think it is time to disentangle simple control of conception by healthy people from the covert attempts to stay the progress of racial disease.

It will be seen from the above, therefore, that on the whole I strongly deprecate douching as a regular practice, but should advise every woman to have a douche available for infrequent use on occasions, when she should employ simple salt and water, or vinegar and water, in making up the douche.

SAFE PERIOD

Many people are under the impression that if the act of union is confined to certain days, they are then quite safe, and that conception will not occur. The dates vary slightly, depending on the exit of the unfertilised egg cell; but, on an average, from the fourth or fifth day after menstruation for about a fortnight a woman is said to be unable to conceive. This may be true for some individuals, whose reproductive vitality is not very acute, but it is extremely unreliable, and in many instances is quite deceptive. The reason for this is obvious to those who know the structure of the parts. Male sperm can live, if it is vital and healthy to begin with, for eight or ten days: during any time throughout this period one deposited days before may emerge from some crevice in the skin of the vaginal canal in which it has lain concealed and swim into the womb and ultimately effect conception, though it is true that the chance of this taking place is not so great as the chance of conception following an active orgasm. Nevertheless, cases are on record when a sperm has made its adventurous journey not merely from the vagina into the womb, but from the outside organs of a virgin girl.

Some people, therefore, to whom it is not a financial disaster when a child is born, may find the comparative security of a "safe period" sufficient. But I am inclined to advise against its observance, because the "safe period" is obviously the time when the woman has less physiological benefit from the sex act, and also because I think that so important and fundamental a need as the act of married union should not be thwarted by waiting for dates on the calendar, when it could be so much better fulfilled at the normal time of desire if the woman is protected in the way which I have recommended on page 35.

"NURSING"

Another "method," often advised by well-meaning people and sometimes by nurses and even by doctors, is for the woman to feel safe while she is nursing her child. Prominence has been given to this advice by the fact that there is a very proper movement on foot at present to encourage so far as is possible the nursing of infants by their own mothers. One fears sometimes that well-meaning but insufficiently instructed people unconsciously urge as an advantage which may accrue from such nursing that security from too rapid pregnancy which is so pathetically desired by the poorer working women. It is true that very generally a nursing mother does not become pregnant, but too many instances are known to me, when even in the early months of nursing pregnancy has begun, for me to feel that the advice should ever be given without qualification. The security offered is as unreliable as that of the "safe" period. Those interested in that point should read my evidence before the Birth Rate Commission, published in 1920, p. 242, of "Problems of Population and Parenthood."

Another danger of such advice is that the poorer and more ignorant women are tempted to continue to nurse an infant long after the milk has lost its nourishing quality, in the hope of delaying so long as is possible the time when they are liable once more to become burdened with yet another unprovided-for child. So long as the flow of milk remains, it is far too easy for the assumption to be made that the child is having all that it required, whereas this may be very far from the truth, and the infant may be on the highway to rickets and many other forms of general weakness, while the system of the mother is also drained and she is weakened and exhausted needlessly. Every encouragement and inducement should be given to women to nurse their own babies, when they have suitably nutritious milk. Yet one cannot too strongly deprecate the confusion of thought which coincidently urges the nursing period as the "safe" period, although, alas, this is often done by otherwise estimable people.

. . . . .

Of the many other varieties of methods and substances recommended and in use, I do not propose to speak. In addition to direct contraceptives there are a variety of malpractices in use which are most harmful. There is no necessity to specify or to condemn them more explicitly. Those who have read the present pages with attention will be able to appreciate for themselves arguments against their use. Many of them are the sources of the erroneous idea that "all birth control methods are harmful." The *ideal* method is not yet discovered, although those described on p. 35 *et seq.* are absolutely harmless, and generally reliable and satisfactory. If anyone knows of any method better than are now suggested, I sincerely hope that he or she will publish it or will communicate it to me, in care of my publisher.

NOTE.—Both my publisher and I must be excused from answering any letters about the names of the appliances or substances mentioned in the text. As described, they can be obtained from many high-class chemists. Anyone living in a very small village should write to one of the larger chemists or drug stores in town, or apply to their local doctor. As a number of inferior makes are on the market it is important to obtain the best only; failures due to inferior articles should not be attributed to the method itself. (See Appendix.)

My attention has been drawn not only to the inferiority of many articles on the market, but also to the gross profiteering going on, rubber caps, of inferior, sometimes useless makes, being sold for 10s., while the proper price to the public of the best makes direct from the manufacturing chemist is between 3s. and 4s.

A new imposition on women has recently been brought to my notice: a large firm with many branches now demand a medical certificate before they will supply a woman with a cap. Any woman faced with such a demand should cease dealing with that store and obtain her requirements elsewhere, or from the manufacturing chemist direct.

APPENDIX

Appendix

RUBBER caps on the lines recommended on p. 37 have long had the approval of the chief authorities in various countries. They are made by different firms, but unfortunately often in an unsatisfactory form. Since the first edition of this book was published, I have followed up various complaints of failure, or of inability to obtain exactly the article demanded, and have been surprised and disappointed at the variability of the article which is sold as the small check pessary. The relative size and proportion of the cap to its rim have a significance which it may be worth stating. In the accompanying diagrams, A_1 and A_2 are drawings of a satisfactory cap; B_1 and B_2 drawings of a type frequently sold, and in my opinion not only unsatisfactory on general principles, but liable to lead to those failures which have made some people distrust this most valuable method. The points to be noted in the drawings are primarily as follows: The spring ring S and the conical portion C should be in such relative proportions towards each other as is indicated in A, and not as in B, where the rim is too thick and heavy and the conical portion C is too flat and small. There is an interesting physiological reason against so flat a cap, which it would perhaps be out of place here to elaborate. A further point to be noted is that the whole appliance, both rim and cap, should be of very pliable and soft rubber, and should not be withered or wrinkled in the slightest degree. Also the line of junction, indicated down the fine line in the drawings of C, should be entirely secure, and without the smallest thin area or perforation. I have had sent to me a cap, otherwise perfect, in which a minute bubble in the rubber just at this junction had

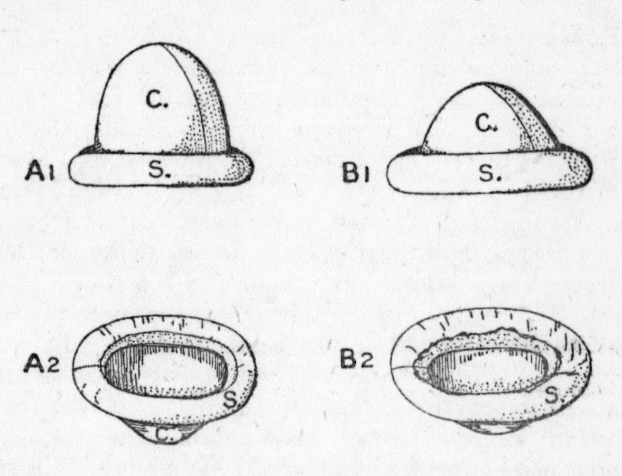

developed into a hole more than large enough for the entry of the sperm. To ascertain that the line of junction is secure, the cap should be held up to the light and examined, preferably by a magnifying glass.

In figures A_2 and B_2 the caps are reversed and shown from underneath, and the line of junction between the soft cap C and the surrounding ring S is apparent. In A it will be noted that the junction is smooth and that the cap and ring merge into one another. But in B there is a comparatively rough welding of the thick raw edge of the cap C, which is—or may be—a very dangerous source of failure. No cap which is offered with such a rough interior should be accepted by a would-be purchaser.

A great variety of shapes and makes of caps are on the market, and those who require further information should study the photographic plates and text of my larger work, "Contraception (Birth Control), Its Theory, History and Practice: A Manual for the Medical and Legal Professions."

It should be remembered that rubber tends to perish, even when not in use, and that to put away a cap dry for months or more, and then bring it into use may mean serious failure, owing to the development of small cracks. Rubber which is not in use is best kept under water, as it is in scientific laboratories. A small china or celluloid pot or jar with a lid should be available, filled with water, under which the cap is submerged after it has been washed out and dipped into a simple non-corrosive disinfectant solution. Time under water may discolour the cap somewhat, but should tend to preserve its essential pliability and usefulness.

Books Recommended for Reading

REPORT OF THE NATIONAL BIRTH-RATE COMMISSION. Pp. xiv, 450. Publ. Chapman and Hall, London, 1917.

PROBLEMS OF POPULATION AND PARENTHOOD. Second Report of the National Birth-Rate Commission. Pp. clxvi, 423. Publ. Chapman and Hall, London, 1920.

BLACKER, C. P., M.C., M.R.C.S.—"Birth Control and the State." Pp. 95. Kegan Paul, London, 1926.

DRYSDALE, C. V., D.Sc.—"The Small Family System." Publ. Fifield, London, 1913.

ELLIS, H.—"Birth Control and Eugenics." Pamphlet, reprinted from the *Eugenics Review*, April, 1917.

INGE, Rev. W. R., D.D.—"Outspoken Essays." Longmans, Green, 1919.

KNIBBS, G. H.—Appendix A, Vol. 1, to the Census of the Commonwealth of Australia applied to the Data of Australian Census (1911). Pp. xvi, 466. Publ. Melbourne, 1917 or 1918. (No date on title-page.)

MARCHANT, Rev. Sir JAMES, K.B.E.—"Birth Rate and Empire." Pp. xi, 226. Publ. Williams and Norgate, London, 1918.

Books Recommended for Reading

MARCHANT, Rev. Sir JAMES, K.B.E., LL.D., edited by.—" The Control of Parenthood." By Prof. J. Arthur Thomson, M.A., LL.D. ; Prof. Leonard Hill, M.B., F.R.S. ; The Very Rev. Dean Inge, C.V.O., D.D. ; Mr. Harold Cox (*Editor "Edinburgh Review"*) ; Dr. Mary Scharlieb, D.B.E., M.D., M.S. ; Sir Rider Haggard, K.B.E. ; Rev. Principal A. E. Garvie, M.A., D.D. ; Rev. F. B. Meyer, B.A., D.D. ; Dr. Marie Stopes, D.Sc., Ph.D., F.L.S. Introduction by The Bishop of Birmingham. Publ. G. P. Putnam's Sons, Ltd., London, 1920.

A PRIEST OF THE CHURCH OF ENGLAND.—" The Morality of Birth Control and Kindred Sex Subjects." Pp. 270. Publ. John Bale, Sons and Danielsson, Ltd., London, 1924.

MILLARD, C. KILLICK, M.D., D.Sc., Medical Officer of Health for Leicester.—" Population and Birth Control. Presidential Address delivered before the Leicester Literary and Philosophical Society." Pp. 1–48. Publ. Thornley, Leicester, 1917.

QUEEN'S HALL MEETING ON CONSTRUCTIVE BIRTH CONTROL. Speeches and Impressions. Pp. 47. Publ. G. P. Putnam's Sons, Ltd., London, 1921.

STOPES, MARIE C., D.Sc., Ph.D.—" Married Love." Pp. xvii, 116. Publ. A. C. Fifield, London, 1918. Eighteenth edition, revised and enlarged. Pp. 1–189. Publ. G. P. Putnam's Sons, Ltd., London, 1927.

STOPES, MARIE C., D.Sc., Ph.D.—" Radiant Motherhood." Pp. ix, 236. Publ. G. P. Putnam's Sons, Ltd., London, 1920. Fourth edition.

Books Recommended for Reading

STOPES, MARIE C., D.Sc., Ph.D.—"Early Days of Birth Control." Pp. 32. Publ. G. P. Putnam's Sons, Ltd., London, 1922.

STOPES, MARIE C., D.Sc., Ph.D.—"Contraception (Birth Control), Its Theory, History and Practice." Pp. 480, 5 Pls. Publ. John Bale, Sons and Danielsson, Ltd., London, 1923. New edition, 1927.

A NEW GOSPEL. Transcribed by MARIE C. STOPES. Publ. A. L. Humphreys, London, 1922.

NEW YORK TOWN HALL MEETING: Verbatim Report of Speeches. Publ. Voluntary Parenthood League, St. Denis Bd., New York, 1921.

Printed in Great Britain by
UNWIN BROTHERS, LIMITED, LONDON AND WOKING

SPEECHES AND IMPRESSIONS AT THE QUEEN'S HALL MEETING *on* CONSTRUCTIVE BIRTH CONTROL

CONVENED BY MARIE STOPES, D.SC., PH.D.

ONE SHILLING NET. POSTAGE 1½d.

Extracts from letters read at the Meeting:—

"I have the greatest admiration for the work you are doing, and for which you now rightly claim the support and interest of the general public. . . . I am absolutely at one with you in the conviction that it is our immediate concern to do battle with a great wrong and a great tragedy—the tragedy of the unwilling mother and the unwanted child."—MISS MAUDE ROYDEN.

"Constructive birth control is one of the most far-reaching, the most intelligent, and the most fundamentally sound principles ever put forward, and I wish it well with all my heart."—LADY CONSTANCE LYTTON.

"You and your husband have inaugurated a great movement which I hope will eventually get rid of our C3 population and exterminate poverty. The only way to raise an A1 population is to breed them."—SIR JAMES BARR, M.D., F.R.C.P., etc.; Vice-Pres. Brit. Med. Asn.

LONDON:
G. P. PUTNAM'S SONS, LTD., 24, BEDFORD STREET, STRAND, W.C. 2.

THE MOTHERS' CLINIC

For Birth Control

FOUNDED BY

HUMPHREY VERDON ROE, ESQ.

AND HIS WIFE

MARIE CARMICHAEL STOPES,

D.SC., PH.D.

OPENED

THURSDAY, 17*th* *MARCH*, 1921

LONDON

THE MOTHERS' CLINIC

108, Whitfield Street, Tottenham Court Road, W.1.

ORIGINAL LIST OF PATRONS

William Archer, Esq.
Councillor Margaret Ashton, M.A.
Sir James Barr, C.B.E., M.D., LL.D., F.R.C.P., F.R.S.E.
Arnold Bennett, Esq.
Dame Clara Butt, D.B.E.
Edward Carpenter, Esq.
Rt. Hon. J. R. Clynes, P.C., J.P., M.P.
Mrs. Despard.
The Viscountess Grey.
Sir Anthony Hope Hawkins, M.A.
Dr. Jane Lorimer Hawthorne.
Sir W. Arbuthnot Lane, C.B., M.B., M.S.Lond., F.R.C.S.
Rt. Hon. Lady Constance Lytton.
Sir Lynden Macassey, K.B.E., K.C.
Lady Macassey.
Aylmer Maude, Esq.
Sir Malcolm Morris, K.C.V.O., F.R.C.S., F.Z.S.
Sir Archdall Reid, K.B.E., M.B., F.R.S.
Rt. Hon. G. H. Roberts, J.P., M.P.
Rt. Hon. J. M. Robertson, P.C.
Miss Maude Royden.
Admiral Sir Percy Scott, K.C.B., K.C.V.O., C.B.
Dr. E. B. Turner, F.R.C.S.
Mrs. Alec Tweedie, F.R.G.S.
J. Havelock Wilson, Esq., C.B.E., M.P.

Note.—The Clinic is now open daily, except Saturdays, to all mothers and fathers who come for advice, and also to doctors, nurses, health visitors, and others who desire to acquaint themselves with the practical working of the subject. No charges are made.

Stamped addressed envelope to be sent by correspondents desiring replies.

Dr. Jane Lorimer Hawthorne, *Visiting Specialist.*
Nurse Rosina Thompson, *Midwife in Charge.*

OUR OSTRICHES

THE WORDS OF THE PLAY FIRST PERFORMED AT THE ROYAL COURT THEATRE, NOV. 14, 1923

BY MARIE CARMICHAEL STOPES, D.SC., PH.D.

WITH A COVER DESIGN BY LOW

TWO SHILLINGS NET (*Postage 2d.*)

Morning Post (Nov. 15th).—"And the subject being one of interest to all and to the nation, though many have given it never a thought, and the piece being written with a passionate sincerity, and the character that is Dr. Stopes's mouthpiece being played with passionate sincerity by Miss Dorothy Holmes-Gore, last night's crowded audience listened with wrapt attention, and the final reception, save for one or two malcontents whom Dr. Stopes in a simple, straightforward speech shortly made feel ashamed of themselves, was enthusiastic. There is much plain speaking, but nothing to harm anyone. The piece is admirably acted."

Daily Chronicle.—"Marked by very genuine enthusiasm. . . . The play is a sincere, honest and brave piece of work. It is propaganda in the same way that many good plays are propaganda. It is successful, not because Dr. Stopes has great skill in the art of play construction, but because she has something to say, and says it clearly and directly and without beating about the bush."

Punch.—"Full of excellent humour and irony, admirably interpreted by all the actors."

Observer.—"She succeeds in interesting all but an infantile minority for whom 'art is art' and a 'play is a play,' and who cling to an 1890 notion that art only gains freedom and value in proportion as it becomes divorced from life."

Daily Herald.—"It is *not* dull. It is every bit as thrilling and exhilarating as the best constructed melodrama."

Sunday Times.—"Frankly, I enjoyed 'Our Ostriches.' Here, at least, is a writer delivering herself of something in which she is passionately interested. . . . Dr. Stopes begins in excitement and keeps it up all through. I would rather listen to her than to some languid exponent of a sentimental intrigue for which not even the author could possibly feel concern. In short, I am more interested in Dr. Stopes than in the average concocter of farces, and would, if I may say so, trust Marie sooner than I would 'Trust Emily.' 'Our Ostriches' is well acted."

G. P. PUTNAM'S SONS, LTD.

24, BEDFORD STREET, STRAND, LONDON, W.C. 2.